To my Best Buddy Joe Kro-Art.

You believed in me before anyone else did
and I am so thankful that I can call Ocean
Gallery my second home. Your family
has become part of my family and I can't
imagine my life without all of you.

www.mascotbooks.com

Pip's Guide to Ocean City: Volume II

For more information, please contact:
Mascot Books
620 Herndon Parkway #320
Herndon, VA 20170
info@mascotbooks.com

Library of Congress Control Number: 2019918404

CPSIA Code: PRT0220A
ISBN-13: 978-1-64543-361-3

Printed in the United States

A portion of profits benefit local charities.

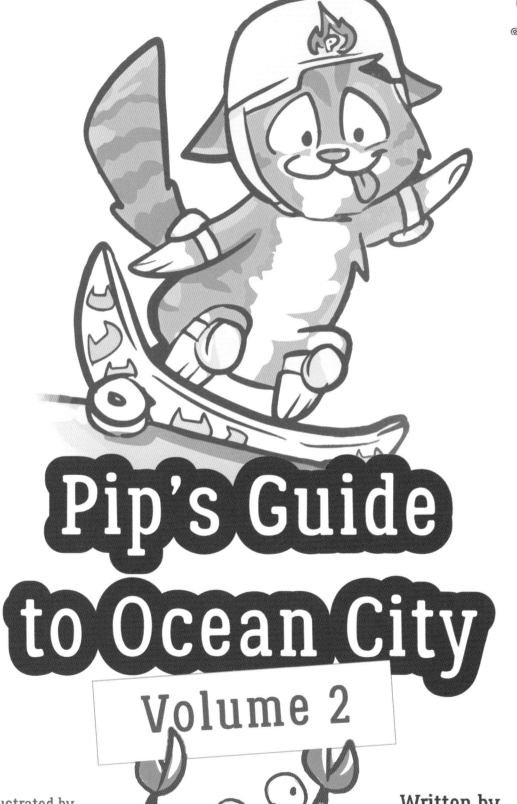

Pip's Guide to Ocean City

Volume 2

Illustrated by

Ana-Gabriela Stroe

Written by

Pip the Beach Cat

My first summer in Ocean City was pawesome!! I met so many people and gave high-fives to little and "big" kids alike. Every night, crowds waited for me on the boardwalk in front of Ocean Gallery on 2nd Street. I was there so often that for a while I thought it was my new home.

Before Ocean City was a resort town, it was home to many animal species we still encounter today. On your visit you may run into one of the world's oldest: the Horseshoe Crab! They look pretty scary, but they are actually harmless.

Sometimes you can see foxes roaming the beach, or, if it's winter, you might even see a seal! Remember to always leave plenty of room for the wildlife.

One day, while I was on the beach, a man approached me in blue shorts with a camera, and asked if I wanted to get my scopes done. I didn't know what this meant but I said, "Sure!"

The next thing I knew, there were shots of me inside these really cool little keychains called Telescope Pictures! When I look inside the little scope, I see me!

If lying in the sun sounds a little boring to you, don't worry—the beach has extreme sports, too! At certain times of the day, you can head out into the ocean on a surfboard and catch some waves. If you've never been surfing before, there are plenty of dudes and dudettes around that can give you a lesson! Just pop into one of many surf shops, like Malibu's!

Ocean City is also home to the Ocean Bowl Skate Park, where you can strap on your knee and elbow pads, buckle your helmet, and skate all day! Then head over to Get Gnarly Skate Shop and grab some local threads!

Safety is really important to me. The quiet little town that I wandered into is booming with excitement and vacationers in the summer! With so many vehicles and bikes coming and going, my buddy Cheswick taught me how to always use the crosswalks so I can be as safe as possible. Before I cross, I always look left, look right, and left again to make sure no vehicles or bikes are coming. Motorists and bike riders also need to do their part by looking up and out for people and cool cats like me!

I also learned the importance of beach safety! I know that if I'm ever caught in a rip current, I should swim to the side to get out of it, not back to shore.

I know that I should keep my paws in the sand until the lifeguard is in the stand. And my lifeguard buddies taught me how important it is to wear sunscreen!

All of us here in Ocean City work really hard in the summers, so it's important that we take time to enjoy everything our area has to offer. One of my favorite things when I have a night off is to sit down to a seafood feast! Do you have a favorite seafood?

A long time ago, Ocean City and Assateague Island were actually one place—but a hurricane came through and created the inlet, which is one of the reasons Ocean City has grown into such a huge fishing harbor. People come from all over to visit the wild ponies that live on Assateague.

At the end of the boardwalk you can check out some of the largest fish ever caught off our coast, including the largest shark! If a real shark scares you, then stop by the shark hanging out over the Ocean City boardwalk instead! Or is that a real one too?!

While you're on the boardwalk, you'll be surrounded by things to do. Every block, there's a new street performer that will wow you with their show! Many have won awards all over the country, but choose to perform here in Ocean City during the summer, like my new friend Kristian Charles, the magician! I don't want to give away his show, but wow was there a lot of fruit!

I know I'm a celebrity, and you probably think that I can go anywhere, but I'm also a cat so I have to stick to pet-friendly places.

While the beach in town isn't pet-friendly all year round, there are lots of other places I can go to play in the sand, like Macky's! It's actually where my pawrents met!

I'm so happy to be living in Ocean City for another summer, and I can't wait to keep exploring my hometown. If you come visit, don't forget to come get a high-five from me!

P.S. If you think your town would be the perfect place for me to write a guidebook for, let me know! I'm always looking for new places to go on adventures.

It's amazing what a little stuffed animal can do for a child in need, an elderly dementia patient, a child with special needs, or a cat-lover that hasn't been able to keep their pet as they transition into assisted living. That is why we set out to make sure that as many Little Pips could make it out into our community as possible. For every Little Pip that is purchased, we donate one to someone in need. To check out our Little Pips head to www.pipthebeachcat.com/store

About Pip

As Pip's fame has grown, he has begun devoting the majority of his time to helping his local community. While you can still catch him enjoying the great outdoors all over the East Coast, you are more likely to find him volunteering at a nursing home, visiting a classroom of kids, or orchestrating his Little Pip Project. Of course, if you want to meet him in purrrrrson, just head down to Ocean Gallery on 2nd Street and the Boardwalk in Ocean City, Maryland, where you might just be able to grab a high-five! His full schedule can be viewed on his Facebook or website. And, of course, you can always follow along with his daily adventures on Instagram.

www.pipthebeachcat.com
@ImFeelingPipsy

Your Memories of Ocean City!